NEXT STATION 2

WORKBOOK

Amanda Cant

macmillan education

CONTENTS

	VOCABULARY	GRAMMAR	FEATURES
UNIT 6 PAGES 43-51	play soccer, watch TV, sing karaoke, play computer games, read books, play board games draw, make models, listen to music, dance, paint, do puzzles	What do you like doing? I like …-*ing*. I don't like …-*ing*. He / She likes …-*ing*. He / She doesn't like … -*ing*.	**Country:** Argentina **Spelling:** ai, ay **Values Project:** Make a Friendship Bracelet
UNIT 7 PAGES 52-58	house, castle, boat, trailer, apartment, cave ocean, desert, jungle, woods, city, country	He / She / It lives in … Where do you live? I live in …	**Country:** Mongolia **Spelling:** igh, y, ie **Values Project:** Make a *Welcome* Sign
UNIT 8 PAGES 59-67	piano, trumpet, tambourine, violin, drums, recorder Sunday, Monday, Tuesday, Wednesday, Thursday, Friday, Saturday	Do you play …? Yes, I do. / No, I don't. Does he / she … on …? Yes, he / she does. No, he / she doesn't.	**Country:** Australia **Spelling:** oa, ow **Values Project:** Make a Promise Card
UNIT 9 PAGES 68-74	airplane, bus, helicopter, car, train, motorcycle Multiples of 10: 10-100	I don't go to … by … I go by … He / She doesn't go to … by … He / She goes by … How many … are there? There are …	**Country:** Thailand **Spelling:** ue, ew **Values Project:** Make a Display
UNIT 10 PAGES 75-83	shirt, pants, skirt, shoes, sweater, sneakers long, short, big, small, old, new	This is …'s … These are … 's … He / She has …	**Country:** Peru **Spelling:** th **Values Project:** Make a Sharing Token

UNIT 1

Lesson 1

VOCABULARY

1 Connect the words and pictures.

1 shout
2 clean up
3 sit down
4 stand up
5 run
6 talk

a

b

c

d

e

f

2 Circle the one that's different. Then check (✓).

1 a

b

c

run ◯
sit down ◯

2 a

b

c

shout ◯
talk ◯

DICTIONARY page D1

· GRAMMAR ·

1 Match the sentences and pictures.

a

b

c

1 Stand up, please.

2 Don't shout.

3 Don't sit down.

4 Run, please.

5 Don't talk.

6 Clean up, please.

d

e

1

f

2 Unscramble and write.

1 nleCa pu, sleeap — C_l_ _e_ _a_n _u_ _p_, p___ ___ ___ ___ ___!

2 tDno klta — D___n'___ ___ ___l___!

3 notD nur — D___n'___ ___ ___n!

4 tSi wnod, epeals — S___t ___ ___w___, ___ ___ ___ ___ ___e!

SPELLING

1 Read. Then underline *ake*.

J<u>ake</u> has a cake.

Now Jake's cake is in the lake!

2 Write *ake*. Then connect.

1 There's a sn_a_ _k_ _e_.

2 J___ ___ ___ has a c___ ___ ___.

3 Now J___ ___ ___'s c___ ___ ___ is in the l___ ___ ___!

MAKE A *POLITE* SIGN

Be polite!

· VALUES PROJECT ·

You need:

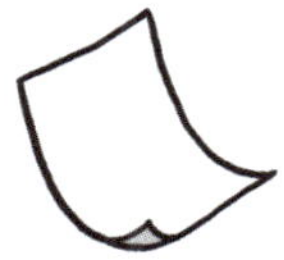

paper

markers

Draw a sign.

Draw a picture and complete the sign.

Write the rule.

Make a display in your classroom or school.

About Me

Are you polite at school and at home?

VOCABULARY

1 Circle the letters that sound similar.

1	B	D / O	4	G	Q / E
2	K	C / J	5	I	H / Y
3	V	B / W	6	P	Z / R

2 Spell your name and your favorite animal.

TRACK 7

3 Listen. Then write the letters in the correct color.

G, J = red **E, I = blue** **K, W, Y = green**

A B C D ___ F ___

H ___ ___ ___ L M N

O P Q R S T U V

___ X ___ Z

DICTIONARY page D1

GRAMMAR

1 Connect the words and pictures. Then spell.

1 chair
2 pencil
3 ruler
4 clock
5 eraser
6 desk

a
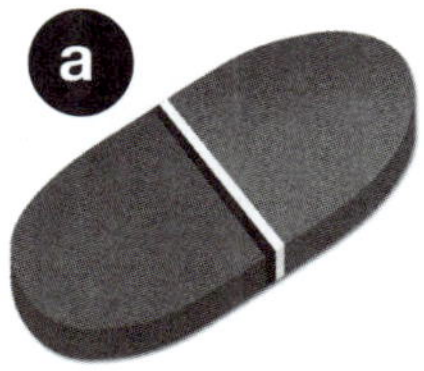
b

c

d

e

f

2 Complete the questions. Then write the answers.

1 How ___do___ you spell  ? _e_ _r_ _a_ _s_ er

2 How do you ________  ? ___ ___ l ___ r

3 ________ do you spell  ? t___ ___k

4 How do ________ spell  ? ___h___u___

UNIT 1

Lessons 7 and 8

LET'S VISIT CANADA

1 Match the questions and answers.

1 What's her favorite sport? (c)

2 What's the national animal of Canada? (   )

3 What's her name? (   )

4 Is a beaver brown? (   )

a Her name's Sara.

b Yes, it is.

c Her favorite sport is ice hockey.

d It's the beaver.

2 Now check your answers on page 16 of your Student's Book.

3 Draw a picture of you playing your national sport. Then write.

Hi, I'm ______________________________.

Look. I'm playing ______________________.

It's the national sport of_______________.

Let's play, OK? It's fun!

UNIT 2

Lesson 1

· VOCABULARY ·

1 Match the words and pictures.

1 morning
2 afternoon
3 evening

a 

b 

c 

2 Write. Then connect.

1 m___ ___ut___   2 h___ ___r   3 s___ c___ ___d

3 Read, solve, and circle.

1 ten seconds + three seconds = thirteen seconds / fifteen seconds
2 seven seconds – six seconds = thirteen seconds / one second
3 five hours + fourteen hours = eighteen hours / nineteen hours
4 eight minutes – two minutes = six minutes / ten minutes
5 twelve minutes + three minutes = nine minutes / fifteen minutes

DICTIONARY page D2

· GRAMMAR ·

1 Read and draw.

1 It's seven o'clock.

2 It's eleven o'clock.

3 It's five o'clock.

4 It's three o'clock.

2 Read. Then draw for you.

1 You're at school.
What time is it?

2 You're at the park.
What time is it?

3 You're in bed.
What time is it?

SPELLING

1 Read. Then underline *ime* and *ine*.

2 Write *ime* and *ine*.

1 It's n___ ___ ___ o'clock.

2 Do you have a d___ ___ ___?

3 There's a l___ ___ ___!

UNIT 2

Lesson 4

·VALUES PROJECT·

MAKE A PLANNER

Don't be late!

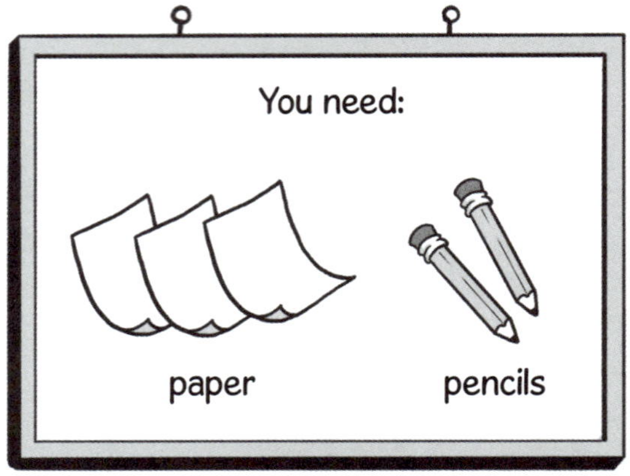

Fold three pieces of paper to make a book.

Make a planner.
Write your name.

Write the days of the week.

Complete your planner with times and activities.

About Me

Are you sometimes late?
Why?

VOCABULARY

1 Write. Then match the phrases and pictures.

1 _h_ave _b_reak_f_ast

2 hav___ ___unch

3 g___ to sl___ ___p

4 ha___e di___ne___

5 ___ ___ to s___ ___ool

6 ___et ___p

a 

b 

c 

d  1

e 

f 

2 Write the numbers in the correct column.

1 sleep
2 dinner
3 up
4 breakfast
5 school
6 lunch

have ...	go to ...	get ...
	1	

TRACK 19

3 Listen and circle.

1 I **go to bed** / **get up** and I **have breakfast**, / **have dinner**,
At the start of every day.

2 I **go to sleep** / **go to school** and I **play**, / **have lunch**,

3 I **work** / **play** and then I **work**. / **play**.

4 I **have lunch** / **have dinner** with my **family**. / **teacher**.

5 Then I have time to **swim**. / **play**.

6 I **go to school** / **go to bed** and I **go to sleep**. / **go to the park**.
It's a busy, busy day!

DICTIONARY page D2

UNIT 2

Lesson 6

GRAMMAR

1 Read. Then look and check (✓).

1

I get up at seven o'clock. ✓

I go to sleep at seven o'clock.

2

I have breakfast at nine o'clock.

I have breakfast at ten o'clock.

3

I go to school at one o'clock.

I have lunch at one o'clock.

4

I go to sleep at eight o'clock.

I go to sleep at six o'clock.

2 Number the activities in the correct order for you. Then write.

a I have lunch at ______________ o'clock. ◯

b I go to sleep at ______________ o'clock. ◯

c I have breakfast at ______________ o'clock. ◯

d I go to school at ______________ o'clock. ◯

e I have dinner at ______________ o'clock. ◯

f I get up at ______________ o'clock. 1

LET'S VISIT GERMANY

1 Read and circle *True* or *False*.

1 Black Forest cake is from Germany. True / False
2 Black Forest cake is a traditional chocolate cake. True / False
3 Black Forest cake has chocolate and bananas. True / False
4 The boy eats cake in the morning. True / False

2 Now check your answers on page 26 of your Student's Book.

3 Complete the chart for your country.

Activity	Germany	My Country: ________
have breakfast	seven o'clock	________ o'clock
go to school	eight o'clock	________ o'clock
have lunch	one o'clock	________ o'clock
have dinner	seven o'clock	________ o'clock
go to sleep	eight o'clock	________ o'clock

PLAY TIME

UNIT 1

1 Read and connect the dots. Then write the letter.

1 shout … talk … sit down …
stand up … clean up … talk

What's the letter? __p__

2 talk … shout … run …
stand up … clean up

What's the letter? ______

3 shout … clean up … run …
stand up … shout … talk …
sit down

What's the letter? ______

4 stand up … talk … shout …
sit down … stand up … run

What's the letter? ______

PLAY TIME

1 Look at the pictures and check (✓). Then write the secret question.

	1		2	
a It's eight o'clock.	✓	t		k
b It's five o'clock.		p		w
c have breakfast		o		a
d get up		o		p

	1		2	
e go to sleep		s		c
f go to school		l		w
g talk		j		o
h have dinner		r		c
i clean up		k		v

Is it ___ ___ ___

___'___ ___ ___ ___ ___ ___?

UNIT 3

Lesson 1

VOCABULARY

1 Look and check (✓).

1

donkey ◯
duck ✓

2

chicken ◯
cow ◯

3

goat ◯
duck ◯

4

chicken ◯
sheep ◯

5

sheep ◯
cow ◯

6

chicken ◯
donkey ◯

2 Look and write.

1 2 3 4 5 6

1 It's a chicken.

2 It's a ____________.

3 It's a ____________.

4 It's a ____________.

5 It's a ____________.

6 It's a ____________.

DICTIONARY page D3

GRAMMAR

1 Look and connect.

1

This is — a duck.
That's

2

These are
Those are
cows.

3

This is
That's
a goat.

4

These are
Those are
chickens.

2 Read. Then circle and write.

1 This is a  . + This is a  .

= These are ____goats____.

2 This is a  . + This is a  .

= These are ______________.

3 That's a  . + That's a  .

= Those are ______________.

SPELLING

1 Read. Then underline *one* and *ose*.

2 Write *one* or *ose*.

1 Th___ ___ ___ are
b___ ___ ___s.

2 Th___ ___ ___ are
st___ ___ ___s.

3 Look at that
n___ ___ ___!

TAKE CARE OF A CLAY ANIMAL

Be responsible!

· VALUES PROJECT ·

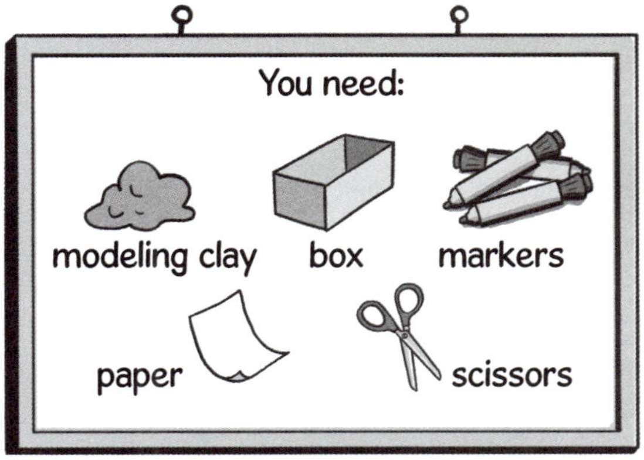

Make a clay farm animal.

Make a home for your animal.

Draw and cut out some food.

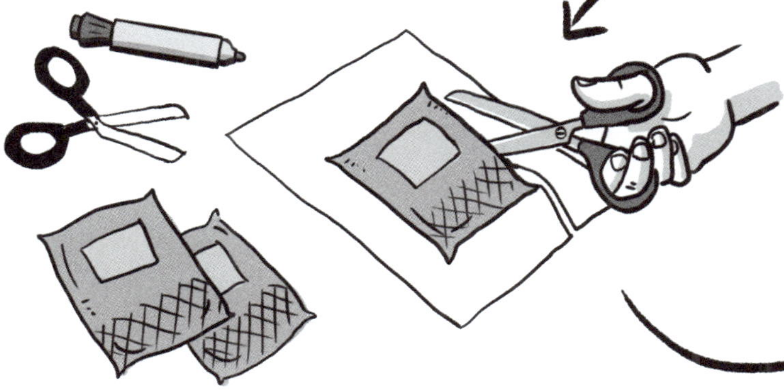

Take care of your animal.

About Me

What responsibilities do you have at school and at home?

VOCABULARY

1 Match the words and pictures.

1	ant	**3**	grasshopper	**5**	butterfly
2	mosquito	**4**	ladybug	**6**	caterpillar

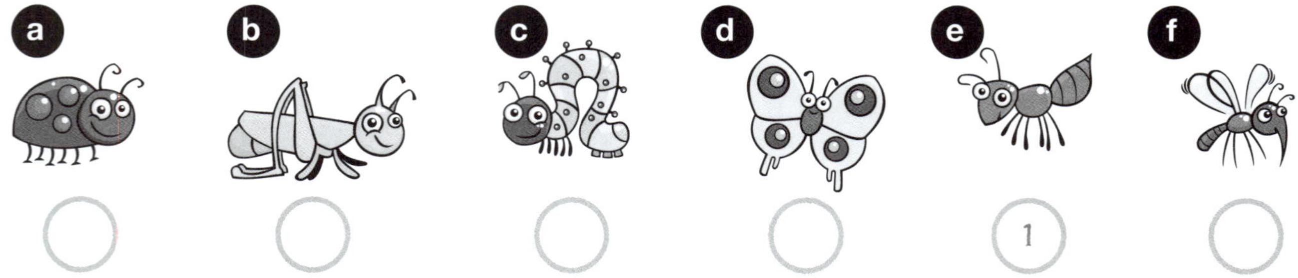

a ◯ b ◯ c ◯ d ◯ e 1 f ◯

2 Count and write.

butterflies
ants
grasshoppers
caterpillars
ladybugs
mosquitoes

How many are there?

1 There are seven mosquitoes.
2 There are three ______.
3 There are six ______.
4 There are five ______.
5 There are four ______.
6 There are two ______.

DICTIONARY page D3

GRAMMAR

1 Look and write.

It's a **They're** **this** **that** **these** **those**

1 

What's ____this____?

____It's a____ ladybug.

2 

What are ____________?

____________ caterpillars.

3 

What are ____________?

____________ ants.

4 

What's ____________?

____________ grasshopper.

TRACK 29

2 Listen and connect.

What are these? What are these?

1 They're green grasshoppers.

What are those? What are those?

2 They're curly caterpillars.

What's that? What's that?

3 It's a shiny black cat.

And what's this? Ooh! Ouch! Stop! Oh, no!

4 It's an itchy, ouchy, itchy, ouchy mosquito!

a 

b 

c 

d 

Unit 3

Lessons 7 and 8

LET'S VISIT KENYA

1 Read. Then write and circle.

flamingos **giraffes** **zebras**

1 What are these? They're zebras.

2 Are they brown and gray?
Yes, they are. / No, they aren't.

3 What are these? They're ________________.

4 Are they birds?
Yes, they are. / No, they aren't.

5 What are these? They're ________________.

6 Do they have long necks?
Yes, they do. / No, they don't.

2 Color the spaces with a dot. Then circle and write.

What's this? / What are these?

It's a / They're giraffe. / zebras.

They're / It's from ________________.

UNIT 4 Lesson 1

VOCABULARY

1 Find and circle the words. Then write.

1 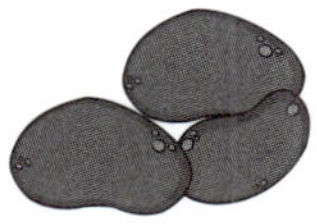

potatoes

2 

______

3 

______

4 

______

5 

______

6 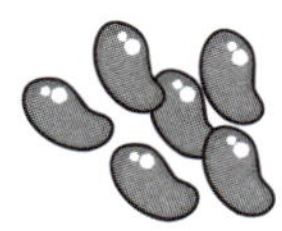

______

p	o	t	a	t	o	e	s
e	h	o	s	o	c	o	e
p	n	m	i	w	s	n	p
b	e	a	n	s	s	i	c
u	r	t	k	p	o	o	a
m	e	o	t	l	r	n	r
t	s	e	e	d	q	s	r
t	e	s	a	l	a	y	o
f	e	b	i	r	c	v	t
b	p	e	p	p	e	r	s

2 Look and write.

Those **These**

1 These are potatoes.

2 Those ______.

3 ______.

4 ______.

5 ______.

6 ______.

DICTIONARY page D4

· GRAMMAR ·

1 Write the questions. Then look and circle the answers.

1 Doyoulikebananas?

Do you like bananas ?

Yes, I do. / No, I don't.

2 Doyouliketomatoes?

_______________________________?

Yes, I do. / No, I don't.

3 Doyoulikebeans?

_______________________________?

Yes, I do. / No, I don't.

4 Doyoulikeapples?

_______________________________?

Yes, I do. / No, I don't.

2 Read and write the answers for you.

Yes, I do. **No, I don't.**

1 Do you like peppers? _______________________________.
2 Do you like beans? _______________________________.
3 Do you like potatoes? _______________________________.
4 Do you like onions? _______________________________.
5 Do you like tomatoes? _______________________________.
6 Do you like carrots? _______________________________.

SPELLING

1 Read. Then underline <u>une</u> and <u>oon</u>.

2 Write *une* or *oon*.

1 Good aftern___ ___ ___,
Miss M___ ___ ___.

2 They're sp___ ___ ___s.

3 Do you like my t___ ___ ___,
Miss M___ ___ ___?

Unit 4

Lesson 4

VALUES PROJECT

MAKE A *NEW THINGS* POSTER

Try new things!

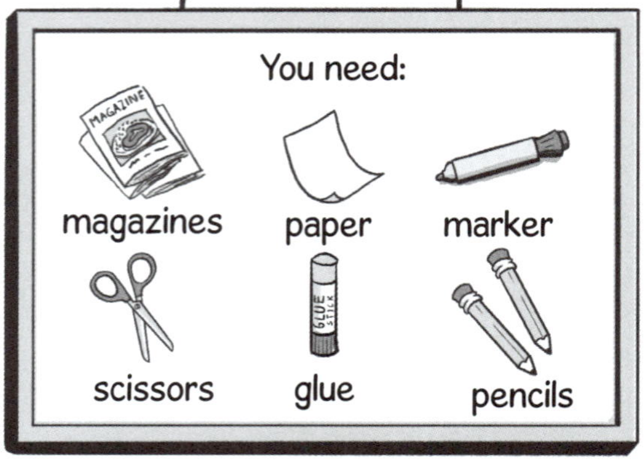

Choose the foods you want to try.

Write: **New things to try this week.**

Draw or glue pictures of the foods you want to try.

Take the poster home.

About Me

Why is it good to try new things?

· VOCABULARY ·

1 Circle the missing letter. Then write.

1 

a / i

p_a_nc_a_kes

2 

e / a

Fr___nch fri___s

3 

t / r

hambu___ge___s

4 

s / t

___andwiche___

5 

p / c

ice ___o___s

6 

o / e

c___ ___kies

2 Look at Activity 1. Write the snacks in the order that you like them.

1 ____________________

2 ____________________

3 ____________________

4 ____________________

5 ____________________

6 ____________________

DICTIONARY page D4

UNIT 4

Lesson 6

GRAMMAR

1 Look and write.

I like **I don't like**

1

___________ carrots.

2

___________ pancakes.

3

___________ ice pops.

4

___________ hamburgers.

TRACK 37

2 Listen and write. Then connect.

1 Do you like h_a_ _m_ _b_u_r_ _g_e_r_ _s_?

2 Do you like ___ ___n___ ___ ___s?

3 Do you like everything?

a No, I don't. No, I don't. I don't like spiders and I don't like snakes!

b Yes, I do. Yes, I do. I like ___ ___ ___b___r___ ___ ___ ___ with ___ ___io___ ___.

c Yes, I do. Yes, I do. I like ___a___a___ ___ ___ with hot p___ ___c___ ___ ___ ___.

LET'S VISIT TURKEY

1 Match the questions and answers.

1 What's Turkish delight?  ◯

2 Is Ahmet's dad a teacher? ◯

3 Does he have pancakes on his stand? ◯

4 Does he have peppers? ◯

a No, he isn't.

b No, he doesn't.

c Yes, he does.

d It's a candy.

2 Now check your answers on page 50 of your Student's Book.

3 Draw vegetables from your country. Then write.

potatoes	**carrots**
peppers	**onions**
beans	**tomatoes**
I like	**I don't like**
These are	

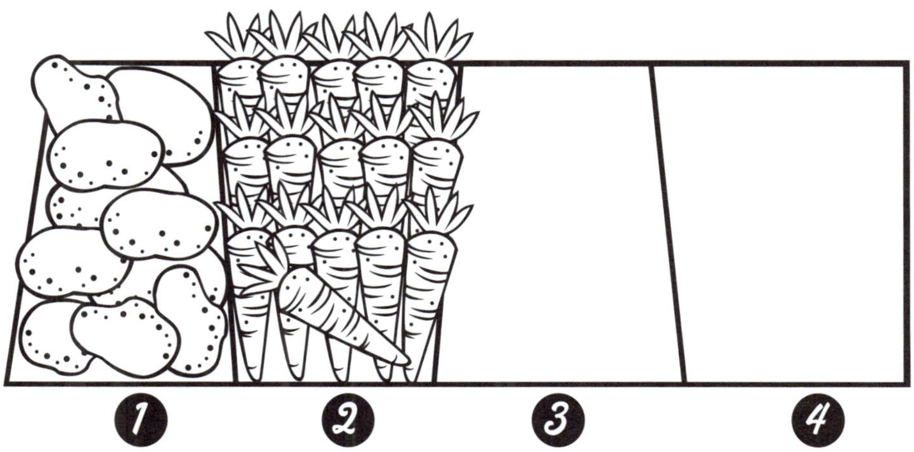

1 These are potatoes ______. I like potatoes ______.

2 ______. ______.

3 ______. ______.

4 ______. ______.

PLAY TIME

UNIT 3

1 Complete the puzzles.

Puzzle a

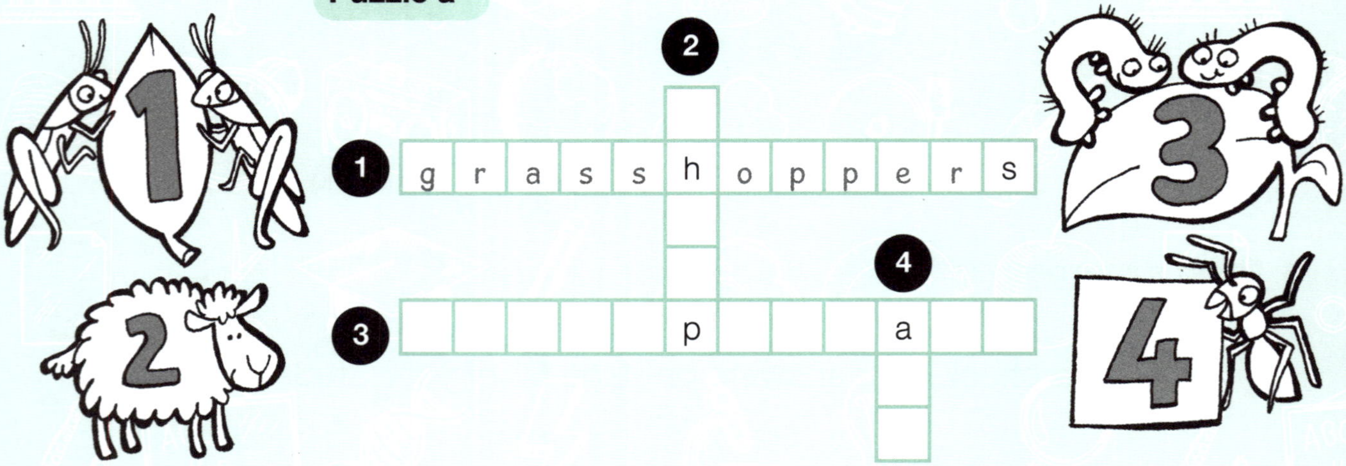

Puzzle b

PLAY TIME

UNIT 4

1 Look and check (✓) the things in the picture.

potatoes ✓	peppers ○	carrots ○	sandwiches ○
ice pops ○	pancakes ○	chickens ○	cows ○
ducks ○	onions ○	goats ○	tomatoes ○

2 Look at Activity 1. Complete the chart for you.

I like … ☺	I don't like … ☹
potatoes	

Unit 5 Lesson 1

VOCABULARY

1 Match the words and pictures. Then write.

1 climb a tree	**3** play the guitar	**5** touch your toes
2 speak Vietnamese	**4** do taekwondo	**6** jump rope

a 

____

b 

____

c 

____

d 

____

e  1

climb a tree

f 

____

2 Write and color the correct squares to complete the chart.

		a	b	c	d	e	f
		Vietnamese	the guitar	rope	______	taekwondo	your toes
1	do						
2	climb						
3	jump						
4	______						
5	touch						
6	______						

DICTIONARY page D5

GRAMMAR

1 Read. Then look and write.

Yes, I can. **No, I can't.**

1 Can you touch your toes?

2 Can you climb a tree?

3 Can you play the guitar?

4 Can you jump rope?

2 Complete the questions. Then check (✓) for you.

		Yes, I can.	No, I can't.
1	Can you touch your toes?	○	○
2	______ speak Vietnamese?	○	○
3	______ play the guitar?	○	○
4	______ climb a tree?	○	○

UNIT 5

Lesson 3

· SPELLING ·

1 Read. Then underline ea and ee.

In the morning, I go to school. I like my teacher.

I have lunch under a tree.

I go home at three o'clock in the afternoon.

2 Write *ea* or *ee*.

1 I like my t___ ___cher.
"Rep___ ___t after me."

2 I have lunch under a tr___ ___.

3 I go home at thr___ ___ o'clock.

MAKE AN *I CAN* COLLAGE

Be positive!

· VALUES PROJECT ·

Cut out pictures of things you can do.

Write: **Things I can do.**

Glue your pictures. Display the collage on the wall.

Ask a friend: **What can you do?**

About Me

What can you do without asking adults for help?

UNIT 5

Lesson 5

VOCABULARY

1 Circle the words and write. Then connect.

1 lkwalkakl = w a l k

2 hpohophp = ___ ___ ___

3 misswimi = ___ ___ ___ ___

4 deridedir a orhhorsese =
___ ___ ___ ___ ___ ___ ___ ___ ___ ___

5 lyffly = ___ ___ ___

6 ngssingisg = ___ ___ ___ ___

2 Read. Then look and write.

Yes, I can. **No, I can't.**

1

2

3

4

DICTIONARY page D5

GRAMMAR

1 Read and circle *True* or *False*. Correct the false sentences.

1

Goats can't run. True / False (circled: False)

Goats can run.

2

Chickens can't swim. True / False

______________________________.

3

Cows can hop. True / False

______________________________.

4

Sheep can walk. True / False

______________________________.

TRACK 46

2 Listen, read, and connect in the correct order.

- I can speak Vietnamese,
- I can do taekwondo.
- I can touch my big toe.
- But I can't, no, I can't,
- I can swim, I can hop,
- I can play the guitar,
- I just can't fly!
- I can jump up high.

UNIT 5

Lessons 7 and 8

LET'S VISIT SOUTH KOREA

1 Write the words. Then complete the answer.

 = My  = is  = your

 = favorite  = What's  = festival

What's ______ ______ ______?

______ ______ ______ ______ ______.

2 Read and write the answers.

Yes, they can. **No, they can't.**

At your favorite festival ...

1 can people dance? ______.

2 can they play the guitar? ______.

3 can they wrestle? ______.

4 can they eat special food? ______.

5 can they sing traditional songs? ______.

VOCABULARY

1 Connect the pictures. Then write.

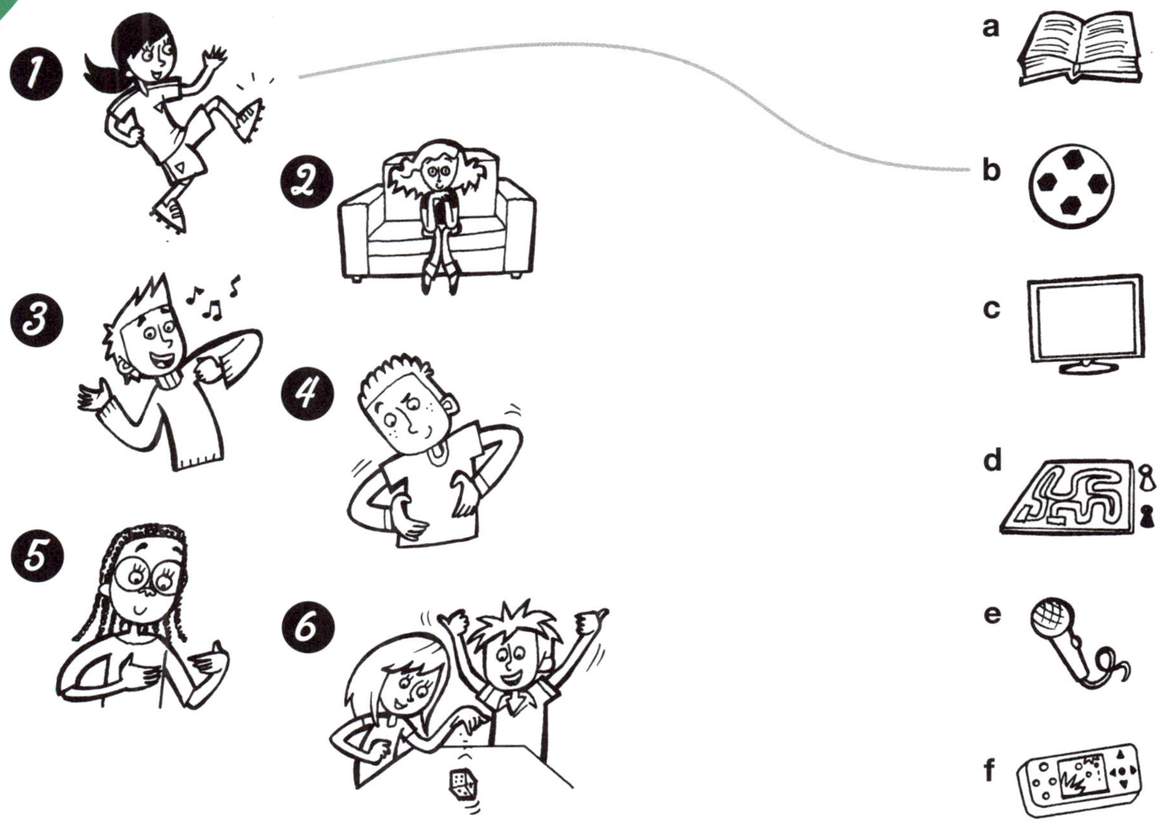

1 play soccer

2 ______

3 ______

4 ______

5 ______

6 ______

2 Write sentences for you.

1 play / don't play I ______ board games every day.

2 sing / don't sing I ______ karaoke every day.

3 play / don't play I ______ soccer every day.

4 read / don't read I ______ books every day.

5 watch / don't watch I ______ TV every day.

6 play / don't play I ______ computer games every day.

DICTIONARY page D6

Unit 6

Lesson 2

· GRAMMAR ·

1 Unscramble the words.

1 

reading I books like

I like reading books ______________________.

2 

like I computer don't playing games

______________________.

3 

soccer like don't I playing

______________________.

4 

karaoke like singing I

______________________.

2 Read. Then look and write for you.

I like **I don't like**

What do you like doing?

1 ______________ playing ______ soccer ______.

2 ______________ watching ______________.

3 ______________ jumping ______________.

4 ______________ playing the ______________.

5 ______________ speaking ______________.

SPELLING

1 Read. Then underline *ai* and *ay*.

2 Write *ai* or *ay*.

1 It's r___ ___ny tod___ ___. Come and pl___ ___!

2 I don't like r___ ___ny d___ ___s.

3 I like pl___ ___ing with my tr___ ___n.

MAKE A FRIENDSHIP BRACELET

Value your friends!

· VALUES PROJECT ·

You need:

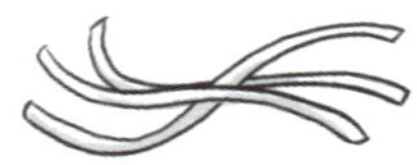

strips of fabric

safety pin

Tie three strips of fabric in a knot at one end.

Pin the fabric strips to your pants and braid them.

Tie a knot in the other end.

Exchange bracelets with a friend.

About Me

What special things do you do for your friends?

VOCABULARY

1 Match the words and pictures. Then write.

1 listen to music	**3** draw	**5** dance
2 paint	**4** do puzzles	**6** make models

a

○
____

b

○
____

c

○
____

d

(1)
listen to music

e

○
____

f

○
____

2 Look and circle *True* or *False*. Correct the false sentences.

1

2

3

4

1 I like listening to music. True / (False) I like painting.
2 I like painting. True / False ______________________.
3 I like making models. True / False ______________________.
4 I like dancing. True / False ______________________.

DICTIONARY
page D6

UNIT 6

Lesson 6

· GRAMMAR ·

1 Look and connect.

1

She likes — listening to music.
She doesn't like

2

He likes
He doesn't like
playing soccer.

3

She likes
She doesn't like
swimming.

4

He likes
He doesn't like
reading.

TRACK 56

2 Listen and circle.

1 He likes **playing soccer at school.** / **reading books at school.**

2 She likes **swimming in the pool.** / **reading books at school.**

But they both like playing with friends.
They both like playing with friends.

3 She doesn't like **climbing a tree.** / **speaking Vietnamese.**

4 He doesn't like **climbing a tree.** / **watching TV.**

LET'S VISIT ARGENTINA

1 Write.

listening **watching** **dancing** **playing**

Roberto likes **1** ___playing___ soccer with his friends and he likes **2** __________ soccer on TV.

His grandma doesn't like playing soccer!

She likes **3** __________ to music and **4** __________.

Her favorite dance is the tango.

2 Now check your answers on page 74 of your Student's Book.

3 Read and write the answers.

Yes, they do. **No, they don't.**

Do people in your country …

1 like watching soccer on TV? __________.

2 like dancing the tango? __________.

3 like listening to music? __________.

4 like playing soccer? __________.

5 like wrestling? __________.

6 like doing taekwondo? __________.

PLAY TIME

UNIT 5

1 Look at the pictures and check (✓).
Then write the secret question.

	1	2
a touch their toes	✓ s	x
b fly kites	v	p
c jump rope	e	y
d hop	a	o
e ride a horse	j	k
f climb a tree	R	E

	1	2
g sing	n	p
h walk	q	g
i dance	l	m
j play the guitar	i	e
k swim	g	s
l do taekwondo	z	h

Can you s__ __ __ __ __ __ __ __ __ __ __ __ ?

PLAY TIME

UNIT 6

1 Find and circle the words.

puzzles **models** **soccer** **TV** **karaoke**
computer games **books** **board games**

s	e	b	o	a	r	d	g	a	m	e	s	p	m	v
o	h	b	o	o	k	s	q	o	t	v	a	i	y	v
c	n	i	m	o	d	e	l	s	p	u	a	s	l	y
c	h	a	m	e	k	p	u	z	z	l	e	s	o	z
e	r	c	o	m	p	u	t	e	r	g	a	m	e	s
r	k	a	r	a	o	k	e	u	p	m	o	c	p	o

2 Play a miming game. Throw a coin onto a space. Mime the action for a friend to guess.

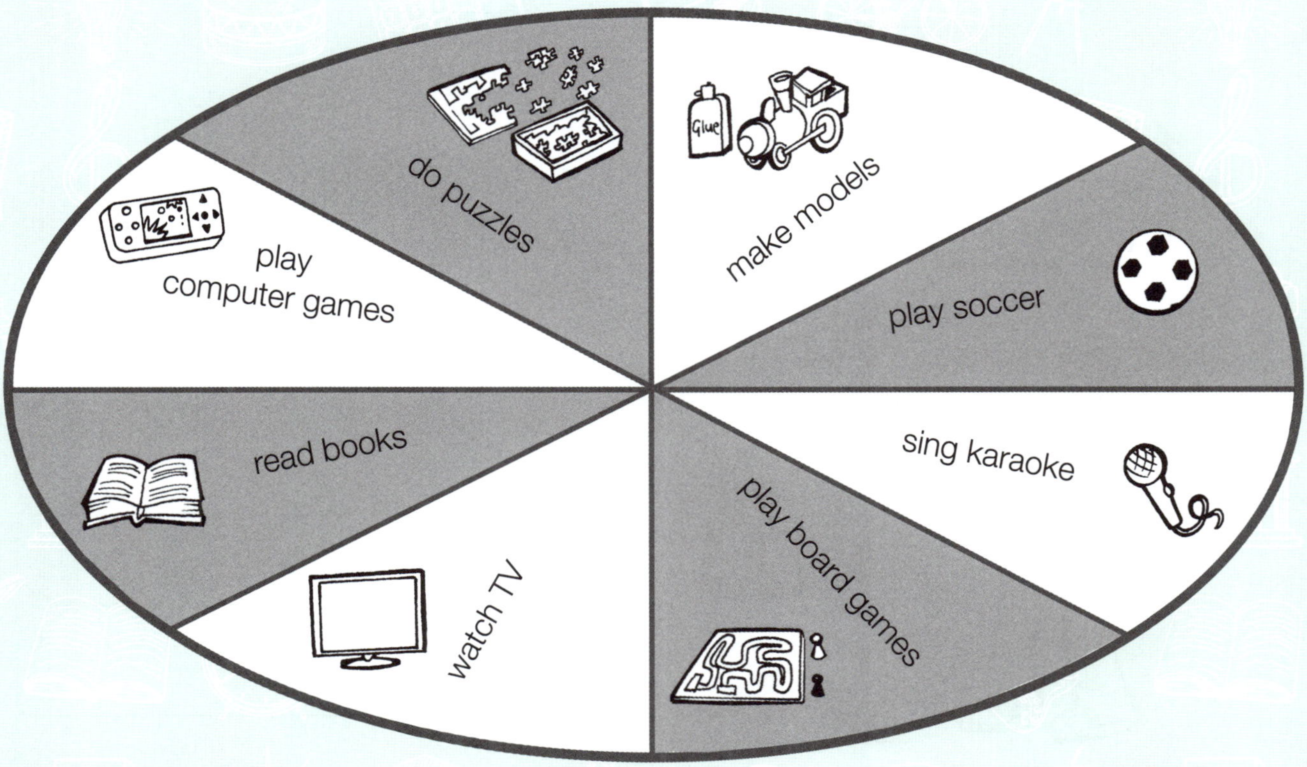

UNIT 7 Lesson 1

· VOCABULARY ·

1 Write. Then look and circle.

1  

a__p__ __a__ __r__ __t__m__e__nt

2 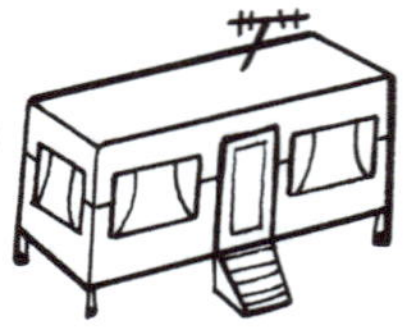 

___ ___ ___i___e___

3  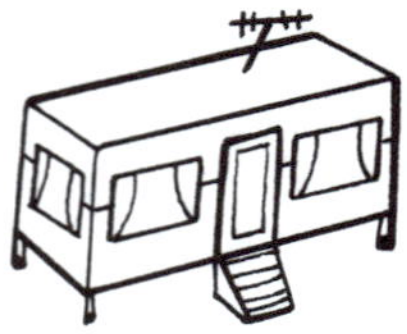

c___ ___ ___le

4  

___ ___v___

5  

b___ ___ ___

6  

___o___s___

2 Look and write.

1 This is my ______________________.

2 ______________________.

3 ______________________.

DICTIONARY page D7

1 Read and follow the paths.

1 She lives in a trailer.   2 It lives in a house.   3 He lives in a boat.

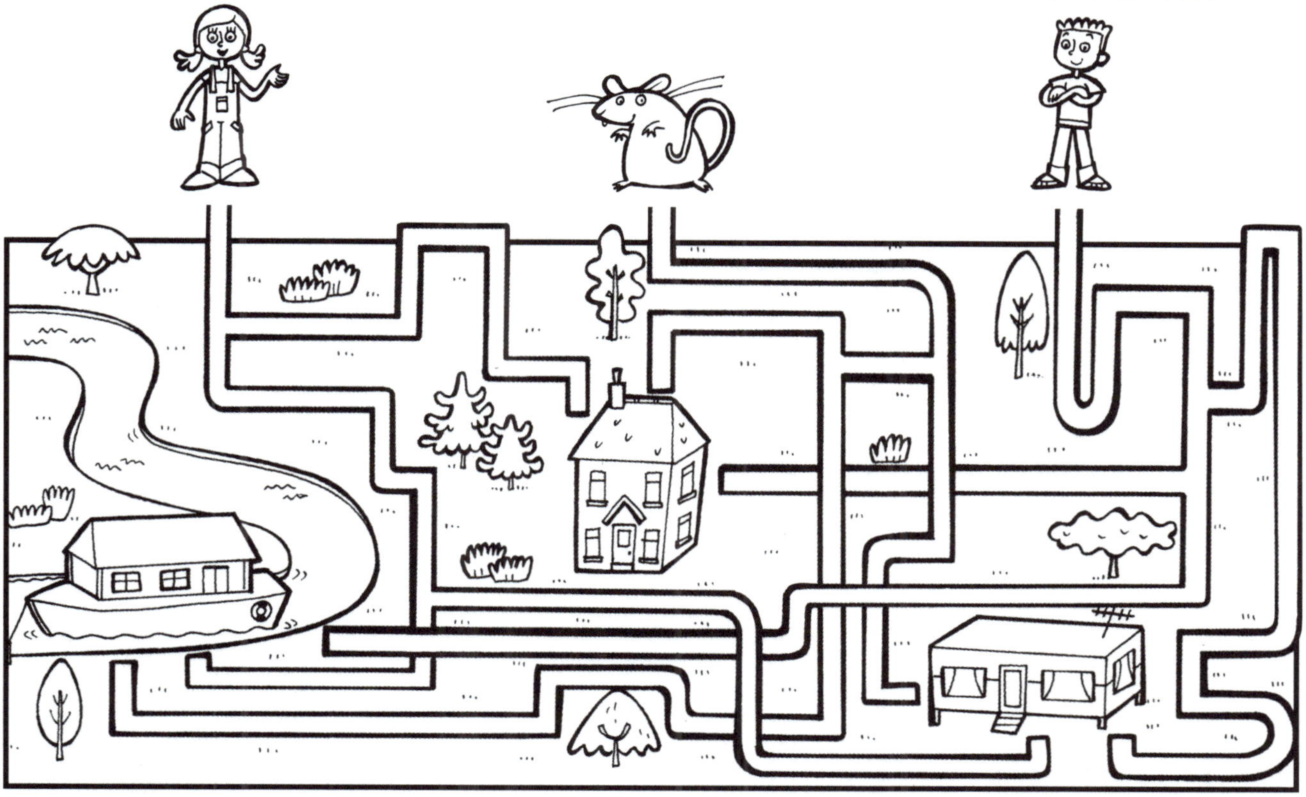

2 Circle. Then draw and write.

1 He / She   castle / trailer

2 He / She   boat / house

________ lives in a ______________.

______________________________.

SPELLING

1 Read. Then underline *igh*, *y*, and *ie*.

2 Write *igh*, *y*, or *ie*.

1 Mmm …
Apple p___ ___!

2 This p___ ___ can
fl___ h___ ___ ___
in the sk___!

3 Stop! That's m___
p___ ___.

VALUES PROJECT

MAKE A WELCOME SIGN

Welcome people!

Write: **Welcome to my ____________!**

Draw your house.

Hang the poster in your house.

Write visitors' names on your sign.

About Me

How do you welcome people when they visit your house?

VOCABULARY

1 Look and write.

jungle **city** **country** **ocean** **woods** **desert**

1 desert
2 ______
3 ______
4 ______
5 ______
6 ______

2 Look and circle.

1 It lives in the **desert**. / **city**.

2 It lives in the **city**. / **jungle**.

3 It lives in the **country**. / **ocean**.

4 It lives in the **ocean**. / **woods**.

DICTIONARY page D7

GRAMMAR

1 Read. Then look and write.

1 Where do you live?

I live
in the
country.

2 Where do you live?

______
______
______.

3 Where do you live?

______
______
______.

4 Where do you live?

______
______
______.

TRACK 65

2 Listen and write. Then check (✓).

1 Where do you live?

I live in the desert.

The ______! The ______!

The sizzling fizzling ______!

2 ______?

I live in the ______.

The ______! The ______!

The splishy splashy ______!

3 ______?

I live in the ______.

The ______! The ______!

The busy whizzy ______!

UNIT 7

Lessons 7 and 8

LET'S VISIT MONGOLIA

1 Match the pieces to the puzzle. Then read and check (✓) the correct sentences.

Puzzle 1

Puzzle 2

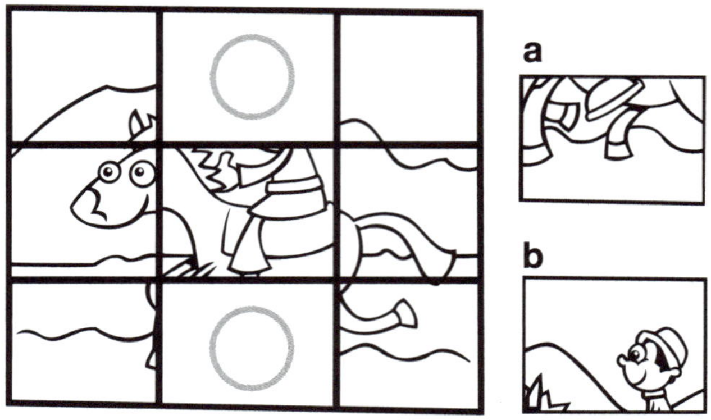

1 In Mongolia, lots of people live in castles. ◯

2 In Mongolia, lots of people live in tents. ✓

3 In Mongolia, people ride horses. ◯

4 In Mongolia, people ride camels. ◯

2 Read and write the answers for you.

Yes, I do.	No, I don't.	Yes, I can.	No, I can't.

1 Do you live in a yurt? ____________________.

2 Do you live in an apartment? ____________________.

3 Do you live in a house? ____________________.

4 Do you like horses? ____________________.

5 Can you ride a horse? ____________________.

6 Can you ride a bike? ____________________.

UNIT 8

Lesson 1

· VOCABULARY ·

1 Look and write.

violin **recorder** **piano** **drums** **trumpet** **tambourine**

❶ 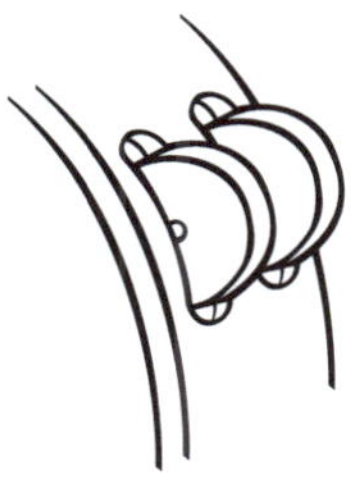

tambourine

❷ 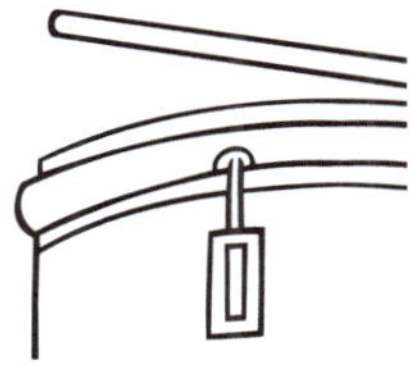

❸ 

❹ 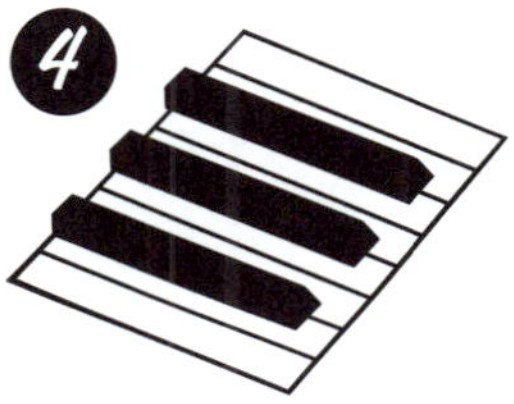

❺ 

❻ 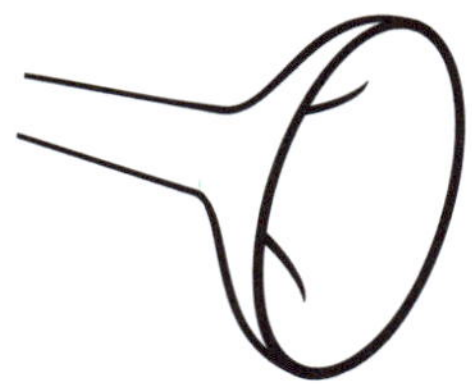

2 Circle the words. Then write the words in the correct column for you.

recorderdrumsviolintambourinetrumpetpiano

I can play the ...	I can't play the ...

DICTIONARY
page D8

GRAMMAR

1 Look. Then read and check (✓).

	Yes, I do.	No, I don't.
1 Do you play the tambourine?	✓	○
2 Do you play the piano?	○	○
3 Do you play the drums?	○	○
4 Do you play the trumpet?	○	○
5 Do you play the violin?	○	○

2 Complete the questions. Then write the answers for you.

1 Do you play computer games? ______.
2 ______ ______ play soccer? ______.
3 ______ ______ play the piano? ______.
4 ______ ______ play the trumpet? ______.
5 ______ ______ play board games? ______.
6 ______ ______ play with dolls? ______.
7 ______ ______ play with robots? ______.

SPELLING

1 Read and color. Then underline <u>oa</u> and <u>ow</u>.

1

Milly the goat has a yellow boat.

2

Milly the goat has a yellow coat.

3

Milly rows her yellow boat in her yellow coat!

2 Write *oa* or *ow*.

1 Milly the g___ ___t has a yell___ ___ b___ ___t.

2 Milly the goat has a yell___ ___ c___ ___t.

3 Milly r___ ___s her yell___ ___ b___ ___t.

UNIT 8 Lesson 4

· VALUES PROJECT ·

MAKE A PROMISE CARD

Help your friends!

Write your name. Then write **I play ____________.**

Find someone to help.

Make a promise card.

Help your friend!

About Me

How do you help your friends at school?

VOCABULARY

1 Connect in the correct order.

Sunday Thursday Saturday Wednesday Friday Monday Tuesday

2 Write the days. Then complete the diary for you.

I ...
go to school
go to the park
go to the mall
sing
do puzzles
draw
read books
watch TV
listen to music

1	S_u_ _n_day	______________
2	M___nd___y	I go to school.
3	T___ ___sday	______________
4	Wed___ ___ ___day	______________
5	Th___ ___ ___day	______________
6	Fr___da___	______________
7	S___t___rd___y	______________

3 Look at Activity 2 and write the answers.

Yes, I do. **No, I don't.**

1 Do you go to school on Sundays? ______________.
2 Do you draw on Wednesdays? ______________.
3 Do you watch TV on Tuesdays? ______________.

DICTIONARY page D8

GRAMMAR

1 Look. Then read and write.

Yes, he does. **No, he doesn't.**

Monday

Tuesday

Wednesday

Thursday

Friday

Saturday

Sunday

1 Does he read books on Mondays? No, he doesn't.

2 Does he play computer games on Tuesdays? ______________.

3 Does he ride his bike on Thursdays? ______________.

4 Does he play the violin on Fridays? ______________.

5 Does he play the piano on Saturdays? ______________.

6 Does he paint on Sundays? ______________.

TRACK 76

2 Listen and complete the chart for the girl in the song.

Day	Activity
Monday	**1** play soccer
Tuesday	**2**
Wednesday	**3**
Thursday	**4**
Friday	**5**

LET'S VISIT AUSTRALIA

1 Look at page 98 of your Student's Book. Circle the mistakes in Bahloo's planner. Then write the correct activities.

DAY	ACTIVITY	ACTIVITY
Monday	draw pictures	play music
Tuesday	play music	
Wednesday	play music	
Thursday	draw pictures	
Friday	play computer games	
Saturday	make models and sing	
Sunday	make models and paint	

2 Use the key to color the picture. Then circle the correct answer.

1 = orange **2 = blue** **3 = yellow**

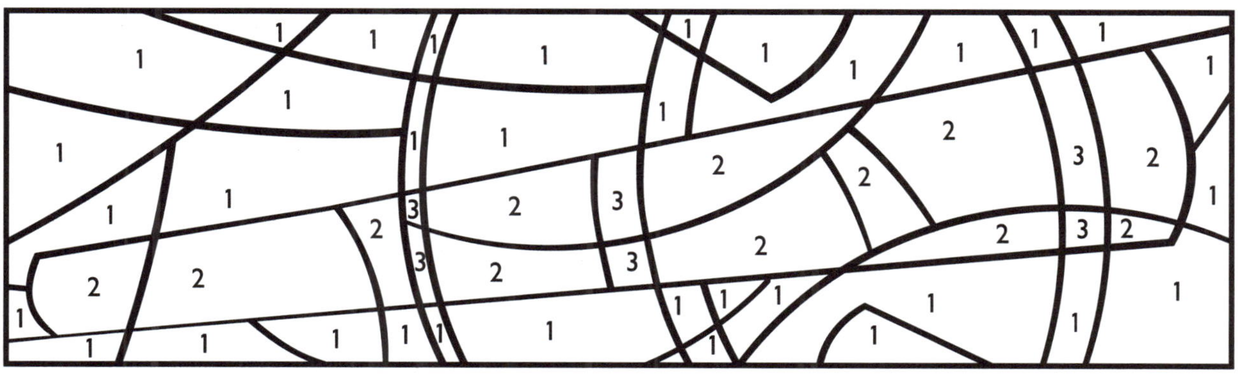

This is a **trumpet**. / **didgeridoo**.

PLAY TIME

UNIT 7

1 Complete the puzzle. Then use the extra word to complete Bubba's sentence.

1

2

3

1 c a v e
2
4
5 o
6 e n
7 r e t
8
9
10
11 a t e
12 e

4

5

6

7

8

9

10

11

12

1 Write the number and draw. Then read and write.

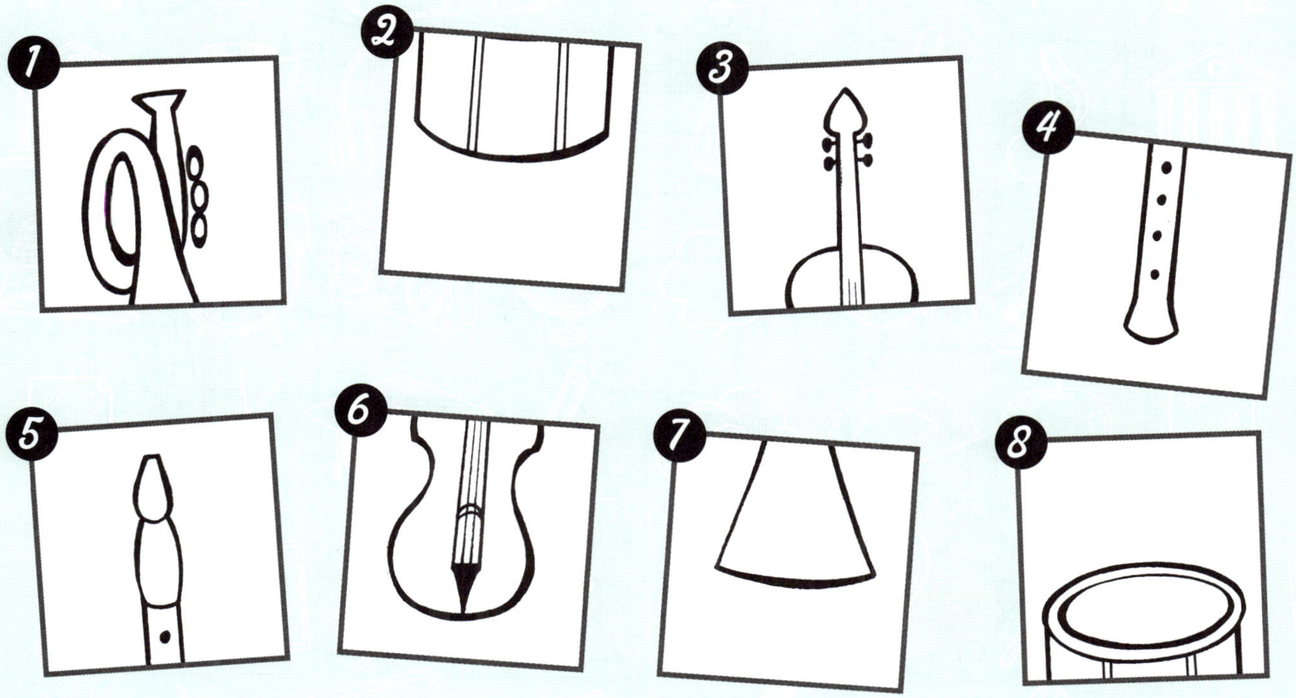

(3) ( ) ( ) (1)

( ) (4) (2) ( )

a It's a violin.

b It's a ________.

c It's a ________.

d It's a ________.

· VOCABULARY ·

1 Match the sentences to the picture. Then color.

1 There's a red bus. (e)

2 There's a blue car. ( )

3 There's a green helicopter. ( )

4 There's an orange train. ( )

5 There's a white airplane. ( )

6 There's a gray motorcycle. ( )

2 Find and write.

1 prehcleito ___helicopter___

2 tirna ______

3 ubs ______

4 rotcoemycl ______

5 rca ______

6 paarlein ______

DICTIONARY page D9

GRAMMAR

1 Read and match. Then circle the pictures using the correct color.

a

b

c

d

e

f

1 = red 2 = yellow 3 = blue 4 = green 5 = purple 6 = brown

1 He doesn't go to the mall by car.

2 She goes to the movie theater by bus.

3 She doesn't go to the beach by helicopter.

4 She doesn't go to school by bike.

5 He goes to school by bike.

6 He goes to the mountains by train.

2 Write.

1 Igotoschoolbycar. I go to school by car______.

2 Idon'tgotoschoolbybus. ______.

3 Hegoestoschoolbytrain. ______.

4 Shedoesn'tgotoschoolbybike. ______.

· SPELLING ·

1 Read. Then underline *ue* and *ew*.

Sue has new blue shoes.

2 Write *ue* or *ew*.

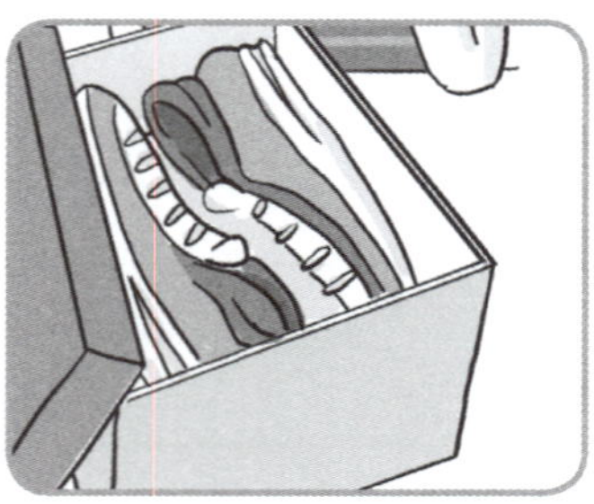

1 Sue has n___ ___ bl___ ___ shoes.

2 I don't like the bl___ ___ shoes.

3 A box and some gl___ ___. A n___ ___ house for my doll!

Lesson 4

MAKE A DISPLAY

Care for the environment!

· VALUES PROJECT ·

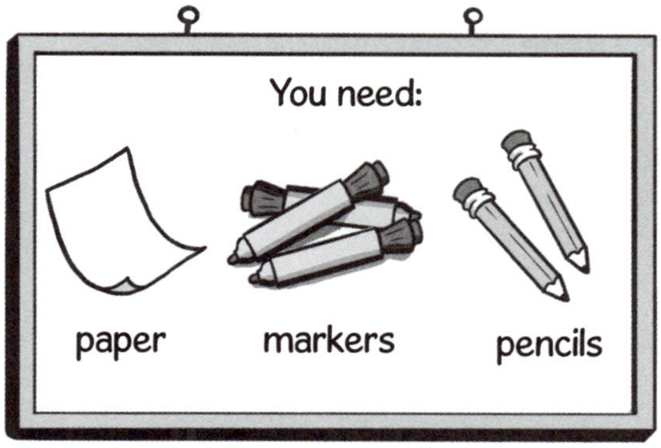

Draw pictures of the environment.

Draw pictures of vehicles that are bad for the environment.

Draw pictures of vehicles that are good for the environment.

Make a class display.

About Me

What can you do to care for the environment?

UNIT 9 Lesson 5

VOCABULARY

1 Read. Then write the numbers.

a 100 one hundred	**e** ____________ fifty	**i** ____________ ninety
b ____________ forty	**f** ____________ eighty	**j** ____________ thirty
c ____________ sixty	**g** ____________ ten	
d ____________ twenty	**h** ____________ seventy	

2 Read. Then solve and write.

1 Thirty and ten is forty.

2 ______________________ and twenty is seventy.

3 ______________________ and fifty is eighty.

4 ______________________ and thirty is ninety.

5 ______________________ and ten is one hundred.

3 Read and connect the dots. Then write.

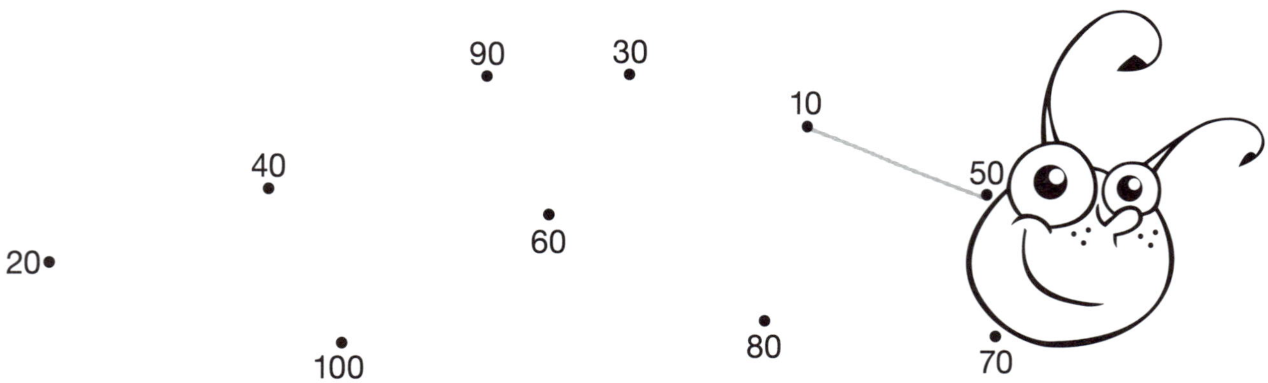

fifty … ten … thirty … ninety … forty … twenty … one hundred … sixty … eighty … seventy.

It's a ______________________.

DICTIONARY page D9

GRAMMAR

1 Complete the questions. Then write the answers for you.

1 How many books are there in your backpack?

There are ______________________________.

2 ______________ pencils are there in your pencil case?

______________________________.

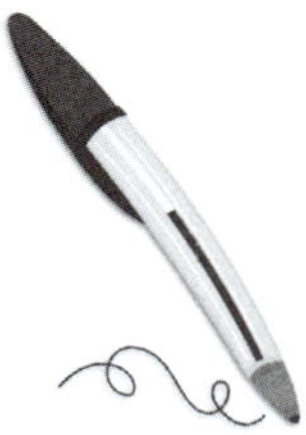

3 ______________ pens are there in your pencil case?

______________________________.

4 ______________ children are there in your classroom?

______________________________.

5 ______________ chairs are there in your classroom?

______________________________.

6 ______________ pages are there in this book?

______________________________.

TRACK 85

2 Listen and circle. Then write.

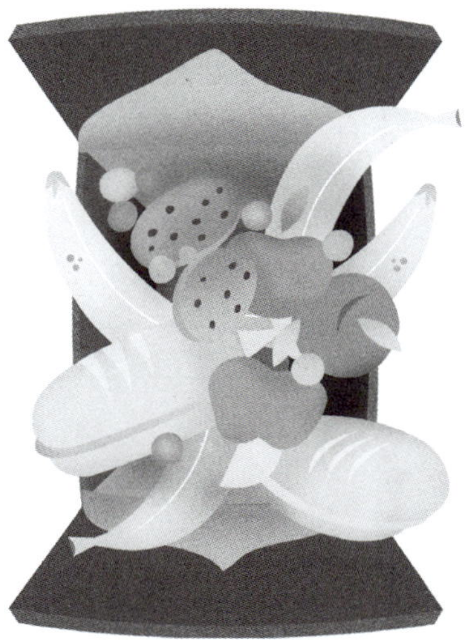

How many apples are there in the picnic box?

1 There are **forty** / **fifty** and **twelve**, / **two**,

That makes forty-two ...

How many sandwiches are there in the picnic box?

2 There are **twelve** / **twenty** and **six**, / **seven**,

That makes ______________ ...

How many cookies are there in the picnic box?

3 There are **thirty** / **fifty** and **three**, / **five**,

That makes ______________ ...

Unit 9

Lessons 7 and 8

LET'S VISIT THAILAND

1 Check (✓) the true sentences. Then write a postcard.

1 Bangkok is in Thailand. ◯

2 There are lots of cars and buses. ◯

3 There are castles. ◯

4 Some people go to work by river taxi. ◯

Dear ______________________,	
I'm in Bangkok!	
Bangkok is in Thailand.	______________________
______________________	12 Washington Street
______________________	New York
From ______________________	USA

2 Write the words. Then draw for you.

 = school  = go 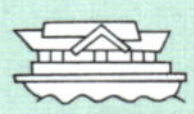 = by  = to  = I

				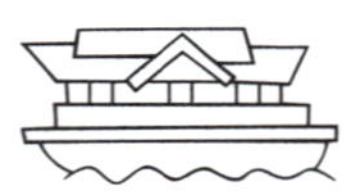
I	________	________	________	________

UNIT 10 Lesson 1

VOCABULARY

1 Unscramble the words to make sentences. Then match the sentences to the picture and color.

1 gray They're pants ___They're gray pants___.

2 sneakers They're blue ______.

3 a red shirt It's ______.

4 skirt It's pink a ______.

5 a It's green sweater ______.

6 orange They're shoes ______.

2 Unscramble the letters and write the words.

1 sseoh ______ **3** tksri ______

2 saeerkns ______ **4** tpnsa ______

DICTIONARY page D10

UNIT 10

Lesson 2

GRAMMAR

1 Look and write.

shoes
backpack
pants
hat
sweater

1 These are ______Hannah's pants______.

2 This is ____________________.

3 This is ____________________.

4 This is ____________________.

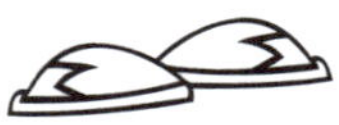

5 These are ____________________.

2 Look at Activity 1. Draw and write.

1 ______________ Ben's ______________.

2 ______________ Hannah's ______________.

SPELLING

1 Read. Then underline *th* in red or in blue.

2 Write *th* in red or in blue.

1 ___ ___is is my family. Do you like our clo___ ___es?

2 This is my mo___ ___er and this is my fa___ ___er.

3 And ___ ___ese are my ___ ___ree bro___ ___ers.

UNIT 10 Lesson 4

MAKE A SHARING TOKEN

Share with family and friends!

· VALUES PROJECT ·

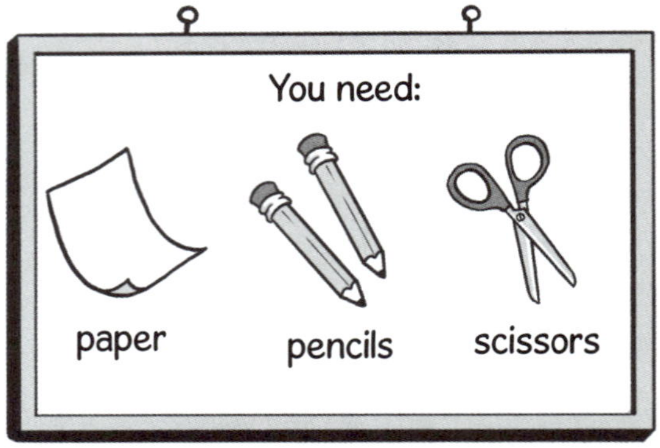

Draw a circle.

Draw your favorite toy.

Write: **You can share my _______________.**
Cut out the circle.

Give the sharing token to someone in your family.

About Me

What do you share with your friends at school?

VOCABULARY

1 Look and check (✓).

1 

It's a	✓	big	✓	shirt.
They're	○	small	○	

2 

It's a	○	big	○	shirt.
They're	○	small	○	

3 

It's a	○	long	○	skirt.
They're	○	short	○	

4 

It's a	○	long	○	skirt.
They're	○	short	○	

5 

It's a(n)	○	old	○	shoes.
They're	○	new	○	

6 

It's a(n)	○	old	○	shoes.
They're	○	new	○	

2 Look and write.

1 It's an ______________

______________________.

2 They're ______________

______________________.

DICTIONARY
page D10

UNIT 10

Lesson 6

· GRAMMAR ·

1 Look and connect.

1	He has	short	sweater.
2	She has	a long	pants.
3	He has	a small	hat.
4	She has	a big	skirt.

TRACK 93

2 Listen and circle. Then write.

1 new / old — shirt / skirt — I have a new shirt.

2 new / old — shirt / skirt — She has an ______ ______.

3 small / big — sneakers / shoes — He has ______ ______.

4 small / big — sneakers / shoes — I have ______ ______.

LET'S VISIT PERU

1 Read and circle *True* or *False*.

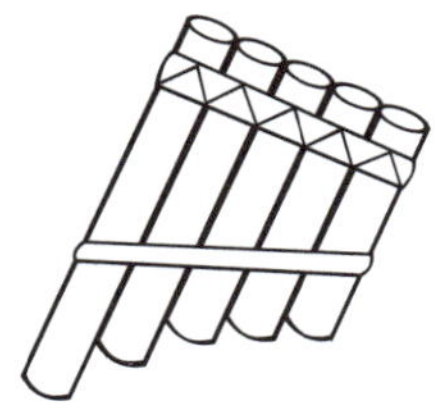

1 Pan pipes are short and long. True / False

2 Guitars from Peru are big. True / False

3 Pan pipes are from South Korea. True / False

2 Now check your answers on page 122 of your Student's Book.

3 Read and color. Then write the answers for you.

Rosa has a big, black hat. She has a long, black and red skirt.

1 Do you have a black hat?

______________________________.

2 Do you have a long skirt?

______________________________.

Xavi has a small, brown hat. He has old, blue pants.

3 Do you have a brown hat?

______________________________.

4 Do you have blue pants?

______________________________.

PLAY TIME

UNIT 9

1 Add and write the number. Then complete the puzzle.

a 22 + 17 = 39 = 

b 13 + 48 = ______ = 

c 82 + 11 = ______ = 

d 17 + 17 = ______ = 

e 25 + 27 = ______ = 

f 51 + 25 = ______ = 

g 22 + 26 = ______ = 

PLAY TIME

UNIT 10

1 Look and check (✓) the things in the picture.

big hats	✓	small hats	◯	backpacks	◯	sweaters	◯
sneakers	◯	shoes	◯	guitars	◯	short skirts	◯
long skirts	◯	a long river	◯	big mountains	◯	shirts	◯

MY DICTIONARY

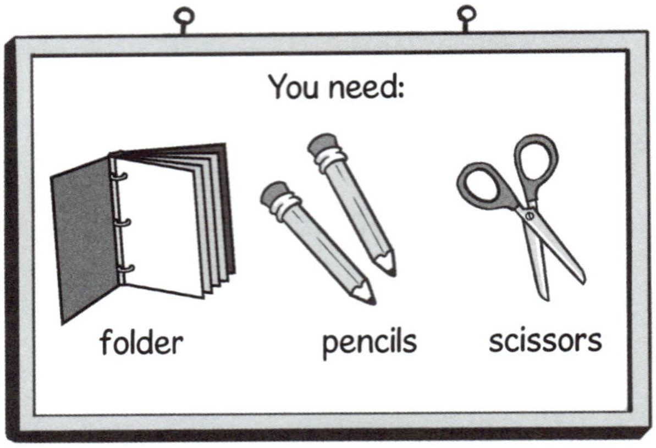

How to Make Your Dictionary

Open your *Next Station* Workbook at the *My Dictionary* section.

Complete the *My Dictionary* pages for the unit.

Cut out the *My Dictionary* pages after all the units are completed.

Keep the pages in a folder and label it *My Dictionary*. Use it to review your *Next Station* vocabulary!

UNIT 1

· MY DICTIONARY ·

Page 4 Look and write.

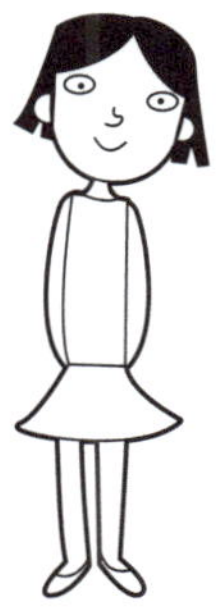

______________ ______________ ______________

______________ ______________ ______________

Page 8 Number the items in alphabetical order.

A B C D E F G H I J K L M

N O P Q R S T U V W X Y Z

elephant ◯	desk ◯	rabbit ◯	farmer ◯	mouth ◯
zoo ◯	lake ◯	watermelon ◯	apple (1)	bedroom ◯

UNIT 2

· MY DICTIONARY ·

Page 11 Look and write.

____________ ____________ ____________

____________ ____________ ____________

Page 15 Write the activities in the order you do them. Then connect.

1 get up

2 ____________

3 ____________

4 ____________

5 ____________

6 ____________

UNIT 3

· MY DICTIONARY ·

Page 20 Write and draw.

____________ ____________ ____________

  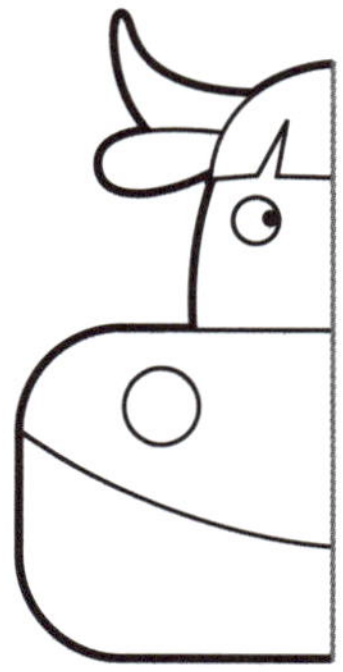

____________ ____________ ____________

Page 24 Look and circle.

ladybug 

grasshopper 

caterpillar 

butterfly 

ant 

mosquito 

Unit 4

MY DICTIONARY

Page 27 Read and draw.

potatoes | beans | onions

peppers | tomatoes | carrots

Page 31 Write. Then use the color key to circle the words in alphabetical order.

1 = red 2 = yellow 3 = blue 4 = green 5 = pink 6 = brown

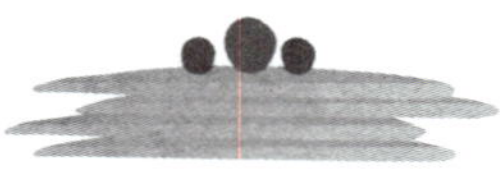

____ancakes

____andwiches

____rench fries

____ce pops

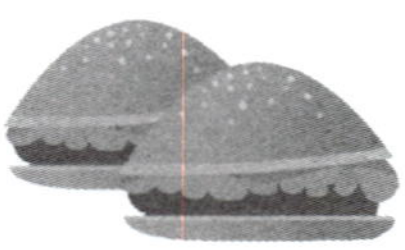

____amburgers

____ookies

UNIT 5

· MY DICTIONARY ·

Page 36 Write. Then connect.

cl___m___ a tr___ ___

sp___ ___ ___ Vietn___ ___ese

___ ___ay the g___ ___tar

___o t___ekw___n___o

t___ ___ch yo___ ___ ___oes

j___ ___p ___ ___pe

Page 40 Connect the letters. Then write and match.

w	o	d	k	**1**	walk
h	a	i	g	**2**	______
s	l	l	m	**3**	______
r	i	p		**4**	______
f	i	n	e	**5**	______
s	w	y		**6**	______

UNIT 6

· MY DICTIONARY ·

Page 43 Draw the missing objects. Then write.

______________ ______________ ______________

______________ ______________ ______________

Page 47 Cross out (X) the one that's different. Then write.

1    listen to music

2   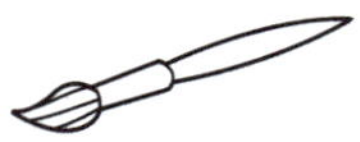 ______________

3    ______________

4 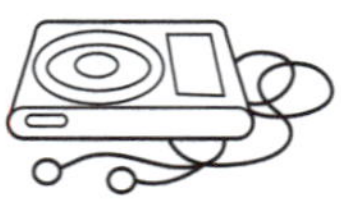   ______________

5    ______________

6  

 ______________

UNIT 7

· MY DICTIONARY ·

Page 52 Read and draw.

castle	house	trailer
cave	boat	apartment

Page 56 Write. Then connect.

c___ ___ ___

___ ___ ___ ___le

w___ ___ ___ ___

___oun___ ___ ___

___ ___ ___ ___rt

___c___ ___ ___

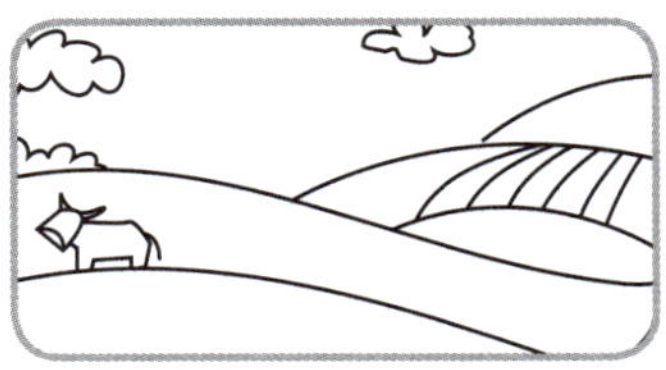

UNIT 8

·MY DICTIONARY·

Page 59 Draw and write.

piano

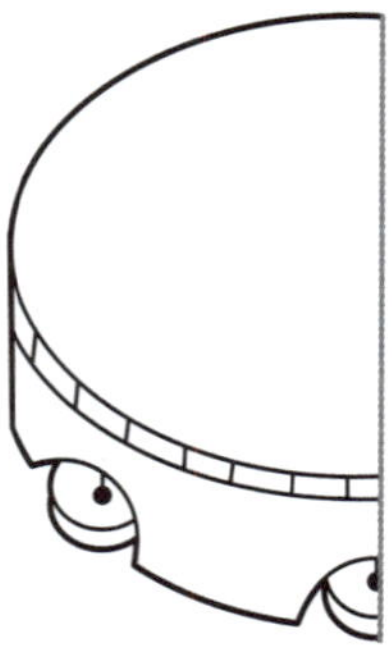

tambourine

drum

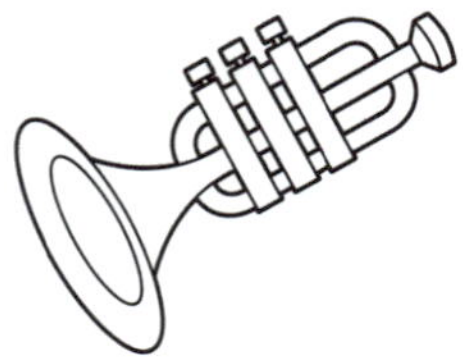

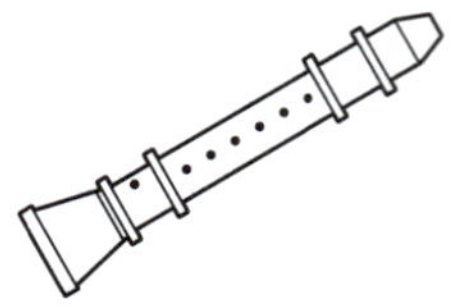

Page 63 Find and write.

1 yauSnd ____________

2 nodMay ____________

3 dTuasye ____________

4 yeesaWddn ____________

5 dhTsauyr ____________

6 ardiyF ____________

7 aaStudry ____________

UNIT 9

MY DICTIONARY

Page 68 Read and draw.

motorcycle | bus | train

helicopter | car | airplane

Page 72 Look and write.

20
___ ___ ___nty

30
___ ___ ___ ___ty

40
f___ ___ty

50
___i___ty

60
six___ ___

70
s___v___n___ ___

80
e___ ___h___ ___

90
n___ ___e___ ___

100
one ___ ___ ___ ___ ___ ___ ___

UNIT 10

·MY DICTIONARY·

Page 75 Look and write.

____________________ ____________________

____________________ ____________________

____________________ ____________________

Page 79 Connect the opposites. Then write.

 big  ____________________

 long  small

 old  ____________________

NEXT STATION LEVEL 2 PROGRESS RECORD

Read and circle.

UNIT **1**

Country: **Canada** / **Peru**
Don't stand **down**. / **up**. Please, sit **down**. / **up**.

UNIT **2**

Country: **Mongolia** / **Germany**
I get up at eight o'clock **in the morning**. / **at night**.

UNIT **3**

Country: **South Korea** / **Kenya**
What are **this**? / **those**? **It's** / **They're** ladybugs.

UNIT **4**

Country: **Thailand** / **Turkey**
Do you like sandwiches? Yes, I **do**. / **don't**.

UNIT **5**

Country: **South Korea** / **Kenya**
I can speak English but I **can** / **can't** fly.

UNIT **6**

Country: **Argentina** / **Australia**
I **like** / **likes** singing but he doesn't **like** / **likes** dancing.

UNIT **7**

Country: **Germany** / **Mongolia**
I **live** / **lives** in the city. She **live** / **lives** in the country.

UNIT **8**

Country: **Argentina** / **Australia**
Do / **Does** he play the drums? No, he **does**. / **doesn't**.

UNIT **9**

Country: **Thailand** / **Turkey**
How many **pen** / **pens** are there? There are **one**. / **three**.

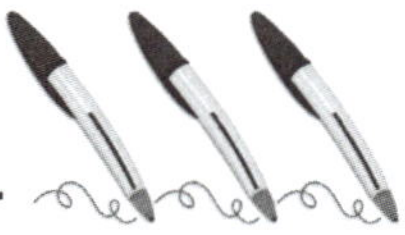

UNIT **10**

Country: **Peru** / **Canada**
This / **These** are Maria's shoes.

Next Station ... Level 3!

Based on *Next Move*
© Macmillan Publishers Limited 2013
Text © Cantabgilly Limited and Mary Charrington 2013
Adapted by Viv Lambert
Next Move is a registered trademark, property of Macmillan Publishers, 2013
First edition entitled "Next Stop" published 2009 by Macmillan Publishers

Director of Languages Brazil: Patrícia Souza De Luccia
Publishing Manager and Field Researcher: Patricia Muradas
Content Creation Coordinator: Cristina do Vale
Art Editor: Jean Aranha
Lead Editors: Ana Beatriz da Costa Moreira, Daniela Gonçala da Costa, Luciana Pereira da Silva
Content Editors: Millyane M. Moura Moreira, Tarsílio Soares Moreira
Digital Editor: Ana Paula Girardi
Editorial Assistant: Roberta Somera
Editorial Intern: Bruna Marques
Art Assistant: Denis Araujo
Art Intern: Jacqueline Alves
Graphic Production: Tatiane Romano, Thais Mendes P. Galvão
Proofreaders: Edward Willson, Márcia Leme, Sabrina Cairo Bileski
Design Concept: Design Divertido Artes Gráficas
Page Make-Up: Figurattiva Editorial
Image Processing: Jean Aranha, Jacqueline Alves, Denis Araujo
Audio: Argila Music, Núcleo de Criação
Cover Concept: Jean Aranha
Cover photography: TommL/iStockphoto/Getty Images, Bubert/iStockphoto/Getty Images, LokFung/iStockphoto/Getty Images.
Illustrations: Gustavo Gialuca (p. 6, 7, 13, 14, 22, 23, 29, 30, 38, 39, 45, 46, 54, 55, 61, 62, 70, 71, 77, 78, 84), John Haslam (p. 59, D1, D2, D3, D6, D8), Andrew Painter | Lemonade Illustration (p. 8, 10, 16, 17, 19, 26, 27, 33, 42, 49, 50, 58, 65, 74, 81), Jim Peacock | Beehive Illustration (p. 4, 5, 10, 12, 15, 18, 21, 24, 25, 26, 31, 33, 36, 37, 41, 42, 44, 47, 48, 50, 56, 58, 66, 69, 72, 74, 76, 80, 81, 95), Melanie Sharpe | Sylvie Poggio Artists Agency (p. 4, 9, 11, 19, 20, 24, 28, 32, 33, 34, 35, 40, 43, 47, 48, 51, 52, 53, 56, 57, 59, 60, 64, 67, 68, 73, 75, 79, 82, 83, D6, D7, 95).

We would like to dedicate this book to teachers all over Brazil. We would also like to thank our clients and teachers who have helped us make this book better with their many rich contributions and feedback straight from the classroom!

Dados Internacionais de Catalogação na Publicação (CIP)
Bibliotecária responsável: Aline Graziele Benitez CRB-1/3129

C23n Cant, Amanda
1.ed. Next Station 2: Workbook / Amanda Cant; [Adapt.] Viv Lambert. – 1.ed. – São Paulo: Macmillan Education do Brasil, 2020.
96 p.; il.; 21 x 27 cm. – (Coleção Next Station)

ISBN: 978-85-511-0138-4

1. Língua inglesa. I. Lambert, Viv. II. Título. III. Série. CDD 420

Índice para catálogo sistemático:
1. Língua inglesa

MACMILLAN EDUCATION DO BRASIL
Av. Brigadeiro Faria Lima, 1.309, 3º Andar –
Jd. Paulistano – São Paulo – SP – 01452-002
www.macmillan.com.br
Customer Service: [55] (11) 4613-2278
0800 16 88 77
Fax: [55] (11) 4612-6098

Printed in Brazil. First print. July, 2019.
Impresso na EGB, 03 2024.